WONDERFUL WORLD OF ENGLISH

Animals Around Us
★
Way Up High

WORKBOOK

World Book International
World Book, Inc.
a Scott Fetzer company
Chicago   London   Tunbridge Wells   Sydney

Acknowledgments

Author: Rebecca Rauff
Editorial director: Michael N. Ross
Editor: Jennifer Lonoff Schiff
Illustrator: Laura Heuer
Production and design: David Corona Design

World Book, Inc.
525 W. Monroe
Chicago, IL 60661
U.S.A.

2 3 4 5 6 7 8 9 10 99 98 97 96 95

Contents

Answers for these workbook activities may be found in the **Guide for Parents and Teachers.**

Animals Around Us

Time for a Change

(Animals Around Us pages 2–3)

A. Number these sentences so they tell the story about Spike.

_____   Spike found the dirtiest places to play.

_____   They put Spike in the bathtub.

_____   Spike was exhausted.

_____   The children were not happy.

_____   Spike's coat changed to black with white spots.

__1__   Spike's coat was white with black spots.

_____   Spike decided it was time for a change.

_____   Spike was all clean again.

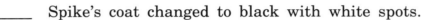

B. Here are four **verbs.** They are action words.

1. decide _____   3. roll   _____

2. return _____   4. wriggle   _____

Look at the story. Find the **past-tense** form of each verb. Write the past-tense verb forms.

> ## Grammar Box
>
> - Use the **past tense** to talk about things that happened in the past.
> - Add **-d** or **-ed** to form the past tense of a regular verb.
>   change/change**d**   wash/wash**ed**

Animal Picture Words
(Animals Around Us **pages 4–5)**

A. Draw a line from each animal to its name.

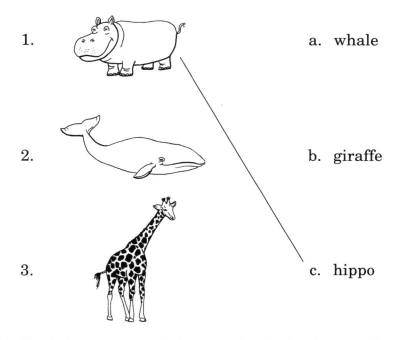

1.   a. whale

2.   b. giraffe

3.   c. hippo

B. Find the names of these animals in the word search. Look down and across.

a	x	b	w	h	a	l	e	f	g
e	t	i	g	u	t	b	v	x	s
l	w	t	r	h	i	p	p	o	n
e	i	l	b	o	g	q	w	i	a
d	a	i	s	d	e	g	h	j	k
o	x	o	g	i	r	a	f	f	e
g	w	n	j	v	e	e	m	i	p
t	b	o	s	t	r	i	c	h	h

dog
giraffe
hippo
lion
ostrich
snake
tiger
whale

Creatures of the Sea
(*Animals Around Us* pages 6–7)

A. Write **true** or **false** next to each sentence. If a sentence is false, change it to make it true.

1. **_false_** Plankton are the biggest animals in the world.

   Plankton are some of the smallest animals in

   the world.

2. _____ An octopus has ten arms and big glaring eyes.

   _____

   _____

3. _____ The arms of a jellyfish can shoot poison.

   _____

   _____

4. _____ The jelly we eat comes from the body of a jellyfish.

   _____

   _____

Grammar Box

A **compound** word is made by putting two words together:

jelly + fish = jellyfish

under + water = underwater

B. Put the clues together to make compound words.

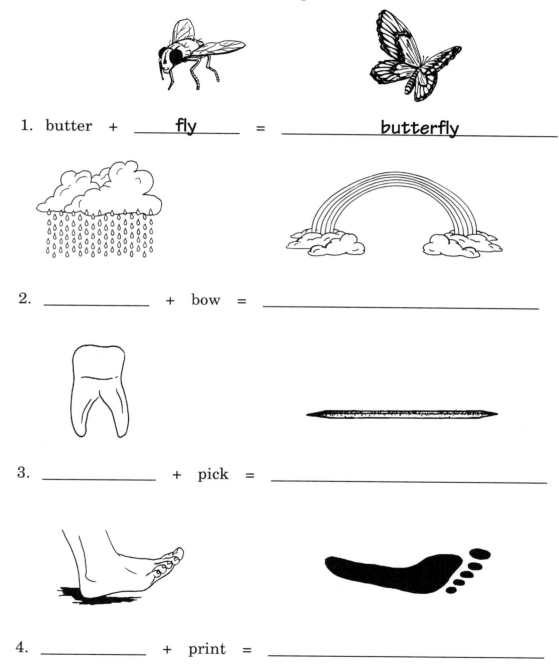

1. butter + ___fly___ = _____butterfly_____

2. _____ + bow = _____

3. _____ + pick = _____

4. _____ + print = _____

Animal Avenue
(Animals Around Us pages 8–9)

Unscramble the names of the eight animals that live on Animal Avenue. Then draw a line from the name of each animal to its picture.

1. e z e n i c h p a m

   ___chimpanzee___

2. n e a k s

   _____

3. n o s e s l i

   _____

4. b u c

   _____

5. s h o i t c r

   _____

6. p o p o p a t h i u m s

   _____

7. n o i l

   _____

8. l i d o o e r c c

   _____

a.

b.

c.

d.

e.

f.

The Story of the Four Seasons
(*Animals Around Us* pages 10–14)

A. What four seasons are described in the story? Write the name of each
   season next to its picture.

1. _____ winter _____

2. _____

3. _____

4. _____

B. Not all parts of the world have four seasons. In some places, there are only two seasons: **wet** and **dry.** In other places, the two seasons are **light** and **dark.** Circle the best answer for each question.

1. When does the sun shine almost all the time?

   (a.) in the light season

   b. in the dark season

2. When does it rain a lot?

   a. in the dry season

   b. in the wet season

3. When is there little or no rain?

   a. in the dry season

   b. in the wet season

4. When does the sun almost never shine?

   a. in the light season

   b. in the dark season

5. What seasons are there where you live?

   a. wet and dry

   b. light and dark

   c. summer, fall, winter, and spring

   d. _____

Poems on Four Legs
(*Animals Around Us* page 15)

Many English poems contain words that **rhyme** (have the same ending sounds). Read each poem. Find words that rhyme with each of these words.

"How to Tell a Tiger"

1. well   _____ tell _____

2. spare   _____

"The Lizard"

3. thing   _____

4. floor   _____

"The Lion"

5. mane   _____

6. roars   _____

"The Hound"

7. hound   _____ _____

8. attractive   _____

Listen to the tape if you need help.

Make Your Own Animal Parade

(Animals Around Us pages 16–17)

A. Here are some directions for making a whale out of clay. Number them so they are in the correct order.

> You will need: • clay   • 1 toothpick

_____   Shape the ball so it looks like the body of a whale. Shape the coil so it looks like a whale's tail.

_____   Your whale is ready for a swim!

__1__   Break off a big piece of clay and a small piece of clay.

_____   Put the tail on your whale. Use the toothpick to hold the pieces of clay together.

_____   Use the toothpick to draw lines for the whale's eyes and mouth.

_____   Roll the big piece of clay into a ball. Roll the small piece of clay into a coil.

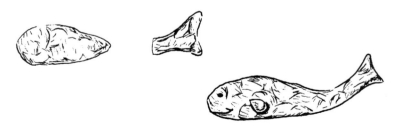

B. Now follow the directions to make your own clay whale. Are the directions easy to follow? If not, renumber them as needed.

The Monster of the Lake
(*Animals Around Us* pages 18–19)

Choose the best word or phrase to complete each sentence.

evidence   Loch Ness   reptile   sea cow
flippers   photographs   Scotland   sunken ship

1. Many people believe a monster lives in a lake in
   _____**Scotland**_____.

2. The lake is called _____.

3. People say the monster has a big round body,
   _____ , and a long neck.

4. Some people think the monster is a _____ from the
   time of the dinosaurs.

5. Other people think it is a kind of _____.

6. Scientists have studied underwater _____ of the
   lake.

7. They believe the "monster" may be an old _____.

8. There is no _____ that a monster lives in the lake.

Swifty and Junior

(*Animals Around Us* pages 20–21)

Which of these animals are closely related to each other? Write their names in families.

cat	duck	lion	spider monkey
chimpanzee	fox	ostrich	tiger
dog	gorilla	owl	wolf

Family 1

_____ dog _____

_____

_____

Family 2

_____ cat _____

_____

_____

Family 3

_____ duck _____

_____

_____

Family 4

_____ chimpanzee _____

_____

_____

Creatures with Two Lives

(*Animals Around Us* pages 22–23)

A. Write **true** or **false** next to each sentence. If a sentence is false, change it to make it true.

1. __*false*__   Amphibian eggs have hard shells.

   <u>Amphibian eggs have soft shells.</u>

   _____

2. _____   The word *amphibian* means "two animals."

   _____

   _____

3. _____   Baby amphibians breathe through gills.

   _____

   _____

B. Here are three amphibians. Use their names to complete the questions. Then circle the correct answers.

1.

frog   Is a ___*frog*___ born from an egg?

   ⓐ Yes, it is.   b. No, it isn't.

2.

newt   Does a baby _____ live in the water?

   a. Yes, it does.   b. No, it doesn't.

3.

toad   Does a baby _____ breathe with lungs?

   a. Yes, it does.   b. No, it doesn't.

Why the Bear Sleeps All Winter

(*Animals Around Us* pages 24–27)

A. Unscramble the answer to each question.

1. Where did Ukko go?
    h e r a t   _____ *earth* _____

2. What did Ukko want to cross?
    v i r r e   _____

3. Who was too busy to help Ukko?
    s h o r e   _____

4. Who helped Ukko?
    a b r e   _____

5. What did Ukko say?
    k n h a t o y u   _____ _____

B. Here are five past-tense verbs from the story. Write the present-tense form of each verb.

1. traveled   _____ **travel** _____

2. looked   _____

3. called   _____

4. walked   _____

5. thanked   _____

> Hint: Take off the -ed to find the present-tense verb form.

Monkey Business
(*Animals Around Us* pages 28–29)

A. Draw a line from each shape to its name.

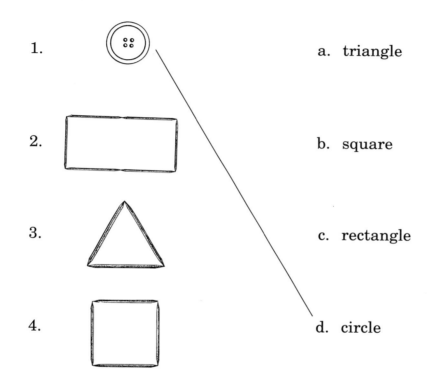

1.   a. triangle

2.   b. square

3.   c. rectangle

4.   d. circle

B. Tell how many sides each shape has.

   1. triangle: __**3**__   2. square: _____   3. rectangle: _____

C. Tell how many toothpicks you need to make each shape.

   1. triangle: __**3**__   2. square: _____   3. rectangle: _____

The Alligator Wiggle

(*Animals Around Us* pages 30–31)

> **Grammar Box**
> - A **noun** names a person, place, or thing.
>   *Examples:* girl   tiger   sky   triangles
> - A **verb** is an action word.
>   *Examples:* runs   think   lived   swim

A. Find these words in the song. Decide if they are used as nouns or verbs. Write them in the correct groups.

aardvark   alligator   friend   jiggled   pranced   wiggled

Nouns	**Verbs**
1. _____aardvark_____	1. _____jiggled_____
2. _____	2. _____
3. _____	3. _____

B. Now find the nouns and verbs in the word search. Look up, down, and across.

```
p  c  d  a  l  l  i  g  a  t  o  r  r        aardvark
r  w  e  p  o  c  l  a  w  s  f  a  d        alligator
a  i  l  g (a  a  r  d  v  a  r  k) e          friend
n  u  g  e  q  i  m  r  b  v  i  r  k        jiggled
c  e  g  a  l  l  o  d  n  t  e  y  s        pranced
e  w  i  g  g  l  e  d  g  g  n  x  a        wiggled
d  i  j  m  z  y  f  a  b  i  d  e  l
```

When All the World's Asleep
(*Animals Around Us* page 32)

Complete this crossword puzzle. Each answer is the name of an animal.

Look at the poem "When All the World's Asleep" if you need help.

Across

2. an animal that sleeps in a cave

5. another name for *insect*

6. animals with six legs

8. animals that sleep in their shells

10. a sly animal

Down

1. animals that rest in holes

3. animals that sleep in nests

4. its home is a pen

7. animals that sleep in barns

9. its home is a den

✔ Review: *Animals Around Us*

A. 1. The story "Time for a Change" (text pages 2–3) tells about a pet named Spike. What kind of animal is Spike? _____

2. Look through your book. Find five other animals that can be pets. Write their names here.

a. _____

b. _____

c. _____

d. _____

e. _____

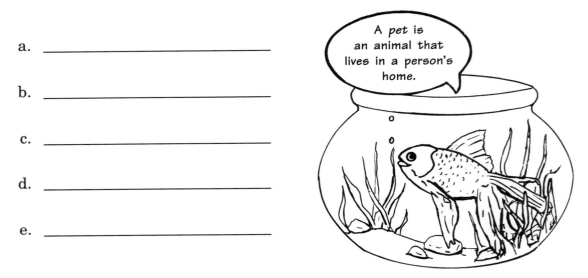

A pet is an animal that lives in a person's home.

B. 1. The animals that live on Animal Avenue (text pages 8–9) are animals that you might see in a zoo. Write their names here.

a. _____   e. _____

b. _____   f. _____

c. _____   g. _____

d. _____   h. _____

2. Look through your book. Find five other animals that might live in a zoo.

a. _____

b. _____

c. _____

d. _____

e. _____

C. Write **true** or **false** next to each sentence. If a sentence is false, change it to make it true.

1. _____   Frogs, toads, and newts are amphibians. They belong to the same animal family.

_____

_____

2. _____   Jellyfish, plankton, and whales all live in the sea.

_____

_____

3. _____   The story of the Loch Ness Monster comes from Greece.

_____

_____

D. Long ago, people created "The Story of the Four Seasons" (text pages 10–14) to explain something that they didn't understand. Which other story in this book was created to explain something that people didn't understand? Circle your answer.

1. "Creatures with Two Lives"

2. "Why the Bear Sleeps All Winter"

3. "Time for a Change"

E. 1. Write the past-tense form of each verb.

a. return _____   d. look _____

b. travel _____   e. listen _____

c. thank _____   f. want _____

2. Now find the past-tense forms in the word search. Look up, down, and across.

d	y	l	b	i	x	m	a	u	e	d	t
e	o	i	w	t	m	c	p	s	a	c	f
k	l	s	e	r	e	t	u	r	n	e	d
n	w	t	v	a	e	d	a	q	e	z	e
a	p	e	d	v	n	c	b	y	t	u	t
h	b	n	p	e	l	o	o	k	e	d	n
t	o	e	i	l	u	y	t	r	e	w	a
q	a	d	s	e	d	f	g	h	j	k	w
l	m	n	b	d	v	c	x	z	e	d	a

Way Up High

Why Is the Sky Blue?
(*Way Up High* pages 2–3)

A. Find the names of five colors in the poem in your book. Write the color names here.

1. _____**blue**_____   4. _____

2. _____   5. _____

3. _____

B. Color the pictures. Use crayons or colored pencils.

1. Color the snowflake white.   2. Color the banana yellow.

3. Color the flower red.   4. Color the balloon blue.

5. Color the tree green.

C. Choose the best word to complete each sentence.

1. The sky gets its color from _____**sunlight**_____ passing through the air. (rainbows, sunlight)

2. _____ are tiny pieces of something. (Colors, Particles)

3. To _____ means to send off in many directions. (explain, scatter)

The First Flying Machine

(*Way Up High* pages 4–7)

A. Number these sentences so they tell the story.

_____ Two men went up in the balloon.

_____ The animals were not hurt.

___1___ Étienne and Joseph Montgolfier sent up the first "flying machine" on June 4, 1783.

_____ The fire began to burn holes in the balloon.

_____ The balloon landed safely after almost 25 minutes in the air.

_____ Next, the Montgolfier brothers sent some animals up in a balloon.

_____ The Montgolfier brothers made a balloon big enough to carry two people and a pot of fire.

_____ The men let the air in the balloon start to cool.

B. What three animals were the first creatures to ride in a hot-air balloon? Write their names. Then draw a line from the name of each animal to its picture.

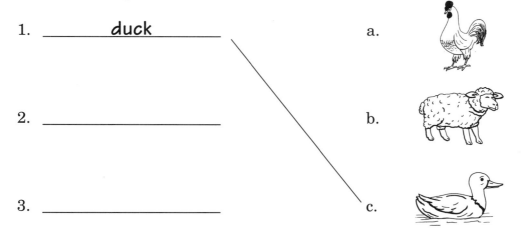

1. _____duck_____   a.

2. _____   b.

3. _____   c.

Poems of the Night
(*Way Up High* pages 8–9)

A. The poems in your book contain many words that **rhyme** (have the same ending sounds). Read the poems. Find words that rhyme with each of these words.

"The Star"

1. star   _____are_____

2. high   _____

3. set   _____

4. light   _____

"Moon-Come-Out"

5. in   _____

6. out   _____

"Star Light, Star Bright"

7. light   _____   _____   _____

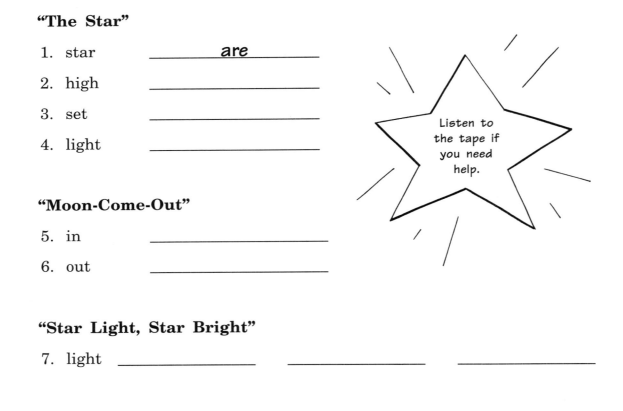

Listen to the tape if you need help.

B. Circle the best answer.

In English poetry, rhyming words are often found

1. at the beginning of the lines.

2. in the middle of the lines.

3. at the end of the lines.

Working in Space
(*Way Up High* pages 10–13)

A. Read each question. Circle the best answer.

1. Where will space stations probably be built?

   (a.) in space

   b. in a submarine

   c. in the United States

2. What will space stations probably be made out of?

   a. scientific work and experiments

   b. solar panels, radiator panels, and metal cylinders

   c. factories and space suits

3. What will people do on a space station?

   a. live and work

   b. take a vacation

   c. wear space suits

4. Why is the word *probably* used so often in this story?

   a. The author doesn't know English very well.

   b. People don't enjoy reading about space stations.

   c. No one is sure what the future will be like.

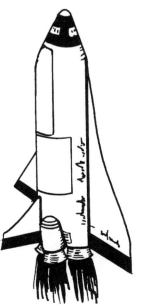

B. Read these words from the story. Write each word below the correct picture.

astronaut   cylinder   space suit
building   space shuttle   submarine

1.

_____ **submarine** _____

4.

_____

2.

_____

5.

_____

3.

_____

6.

_____

The Creatures of Zorp
(Way Up High pages 14–15)

A. The names of the Zorpian creatures describe the way they move. Draw a line from each creature's name to the **verb** (action word) that tells how it moves.

    1. Wiggler   a. glide

    2. Stomper   b. stomp

    3. Hopper   c. wiggle

    4. Glider   d. hop

B. Name your own creatures! Change each verb into a creature's name.

To change a verb into the name of a creature, add a capital letter and -er or -r.

    1. jump

    _____Jumper_____

    2. dance

    _____

    3. skate

    _____

Is That Bird a Dinosaur?

(*Way Up High* pages 16–17)

A. Write **true** or **false** next to each sentence. If a sentence is false, change it to make it true.

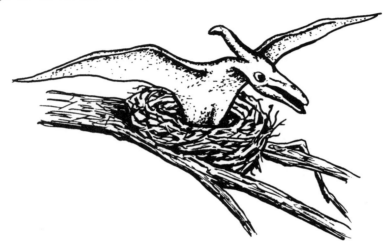

1. __false__   The archaeopteryx lived about 125 years ago.

   <u>The archaeopteryx lived about 140 million</u>

   <u>years ago.</u>

2. _____   The archaeopteryx looked just like a small dinosaur.

   _____

   _____

3. _____   Scientists believe that archaeopteryx was a bird.

   _____

   _____

4. _____   The word *archaeopteryx* means "flying lizard."

_____

_____

5. _____   Some scientists believe that dinosaurs were a kind of bird.

_____

_____

B. Find these words in the word search. Look up, down, across, and backwards.

ancestors	descendants	scientist
archaeopteryx	dinosaur	wings
bird	feathers	yard

```
q   w   e   r   t   y   u   i   o   f   p   l   d   k   s
s   t   n   a   d   n   e   c   s   e   d   j   r   h   g
g   f   d   s   a   z   x   c   v   a   b   n   a   m   n
b   a   r   c   h   a   e   o   p   t   e   r   y   x   i
i   p   o   i   u   y   t   r   e   h   e   w   q   a   w
r   a   s   d   f   g   s   c   i   e   n   t   i   s   t
d   g   a   n   c   e   s   t   o   r   s   j   k   l   m
n   b   v   c   x   z   r   u   a   s   o   n   i   d   b
```

Why the Sun and the Moon Live in the Sky

(*Way Up High* pages 18–21)

A. Circle the pictures that go with the story.

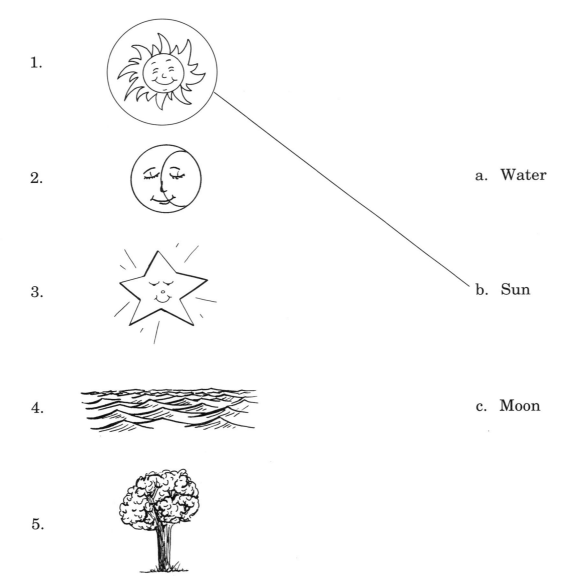

1.

2.

3.

4.

5.

a. Water

b. Sun

c. Moon

Now draw a line from each picture you circled to its name.

Grammar Box

A **compound** word is made by putting two words together.

B. Make compound words using *sun, moon,* and *water.* Put the clues together.

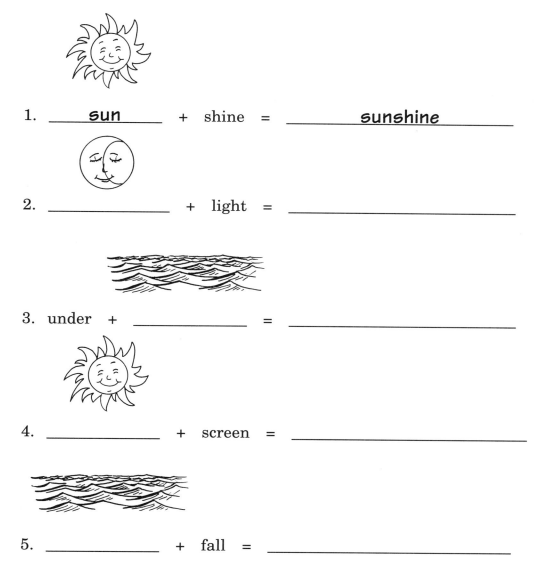

1. _____**sun**_____ + shine = _____**sunshine**_____

2. _____ + light = _____

3. under + _____ = _____

4. _____ + screen = _____

5. _____ + fall = _____

The Flight to Los Angeles
(*Way Up High* page 22)

A. In English, the **family name** (also called the **last name**) follows the first and middle names.

First Name	Middle Name or Initial	Last Name
Margaret	N.	Brooks
Phillip		Lee
Ana	Alicia	Navarro

When we alphabetize English names, we use the first letter(s) in the last name. The names above are in **alphabetical** (ABC) **order.**

To make alphabetizing easier, we sometimes write English names **last name first:**

> Brooks, Margaret N.
> Lee, Phillip
> Navarro, Ana Alicia

1. Write your name:

   _____
   First   Middle   Last

2. Write your name, last name first:

   _____

B. Here is a list of passengers on World Airlines flight 782. Number the names in alphabetical order.

_____ Alberto Rivera

_____ Elizabeth Wang

_____ Gary Goldberg

_____ Kyoko Yoshira

_____ Oscar Pappas

___1___ Michelle Arnaud

_____ Robert Tallchief

_____ Yolanda Jefferson

C. Write the names in alphabetical order, last name first.

1. _____ Arnaud, Michelle _____

2. _____

3. _____

4. _____

5. _____

6. _____

7. _____

8. _____

The Tale of the Kite

(Way Up High pages 23–24)

Complete the crossword puzzle.
Use the clues below.

Across

2. string comes on this

3. cats and kites have these

5. last name of kite-flying scientist

7. leader of an army

8. part of a kite, shaped like a **V**

Down

1. the shape of many kites

2. you hold this while flying a kite

3. what the Chinese soldiers dug

4. people in an army

6. part of a kite, shaped like a **t**

Make Your Own Little Kite
(*Way Up High* page 25)

A. Write the correct numeral next to each number word. These are **cardinal** numbers. We use them to count things.

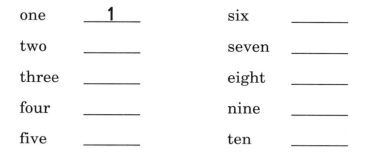

one	1	six	_____
two	_____	seven	_____
three	_____	eight	_____
four	_____	nine	_____
five	_____	ten	_____

B. We use **ordinal** numbers to talk about the order of things.

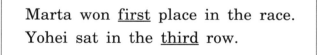

> Marta won <u>first</u> place in the race.
> Yohei sat in the <u>third</u> row.

Draw a line from each ordinal number to the cardinal number that goes with it.

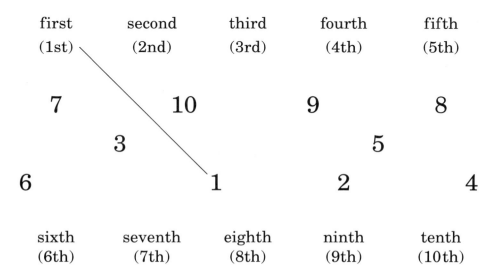

first	second	third	fourth	fifth
(1st)	(2nd)	(3rd)	(4th)	(5th)

7   10   9   8

3   5

6   1   2   4

sixth	seventh	eighth	ninth	tenth
(6th)	(7th)	(8th)	(9th)	(10th)

C. Here is a list of the things you need to make your own little kite. Number them to show which you need to use 1st, 2nd, 3rd, and so on. Use ordinal numbers.

_____   string

__1st__   a piece of paper

_____   scissors

_____   a paper punch

_____   a facial tissue

_____   a paper clip

_____   a ruler

_____   paper reinforcements

_____   a pencil

_____   markers or crayons

If you need help, look at the directions for making a kite in your book.

Poems That Shine

(Way Up High pages 26–27)

A. Read the poems out loud. Listen to the rhyming words. Then complete these sentences.

Listen to the tape if you need help.

"Firefly"

1. Most of the lines in this poem end with _____rhyming words_____.

   (the same word, rhyming words)

2. Two of the lines in this poem end with _____.

   (the same word, rhyming words)

3. The last word in the first line rhymes with the last word in the

   _____ line.   (third, second)

4. The last word in the fifth line rhymes with the last word in the

   _____ line.   (sixth, fourth)

"Stars"

5. Most of the lines in this poem end with _____.

   (the same word, rhyming words)

B. Some English poetry contains **internal** rhyme—rhyming words in the *middle* of a line or lines of a poem.

Which of these poems has internal rhyme? Circle your answer.

1. "Firefly"

2. "Stars"

C. Look at the poem "Stars." Find words that rhyme with these words.

1. bright   _____light_____   _____

2. twinkly   _____

3. red   _____

The Bridge in the Sky
(*Way Up High* pages 28–29)

Write **true** or **false** next to each sentence. If a sentence is false, change it to make it true.

1. __false__   Rainbows are made by sunlight shining through pieces of gold.

   <u>Rainbows are made by sunlight shining</u>

   <u>through raindrops.</u>

2. _____   Sunlight contains many colors.

3. _____   To see a rainbow, you must have the sun in front of you and rain falling behind you.

4. _____   At the end of a rainbow, you can find a pot of gold.

Up in the Air

(Way Up High pages 30–31)

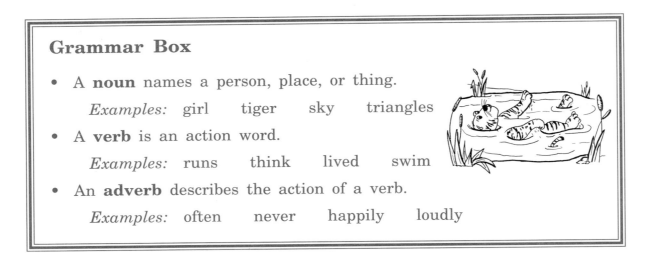

Grammar Box

- A **noun** names a person, place, or thing.

    Examples: girl   tiger   sky   triangles

- A **verb** is an action word.

    Examples: runs   think   lived   swim

- An **adverb** describes the action of a verb.

    Examples: often   never   happily   loudly

Find these words in the song. Decide if they are used as nouns, verbs, or adverbs. Write them in the correct groups.

air	fast	high	low	song
car	float	house	see	up
down	go	look	slow	zoo

Nouns	**Verbs**	**Adverbs**
1. _____air_____	1. _____float_____	1. _____down_____
2. _____	2. _____	2. _____
3. _____	3. _____	3. _____
4. _____	4. _____	4. _____
5. _____	5. _____	5. _____
6. _____	6. _____	6. _____